Project Management

Memorandum of Agreement and Conditions of Engagement

THIRD EDITION

Published by RICS Business Services Limited,
a wholly owned subsidiary of
The Royal Institution of Surveyors,
under the RICS Books imprint
Surveyor Court
Westwood Business Park
Coventry CV4 8JE
UK

No responsibility for loss occasioned to any person acting or refraining from action
as a result of the material included in this publication can be accepted by the author
or publisher.

Produced for the Project Management Panel of the RICS

First edition published 1989
Second edition published 1992

ISBN 0 85406 947 X

Printed in Great Britain by Quorn Selective Repro Ltd, Loughborough.

Memorandum of Agreement Between Client and Project Manager

*MEMORANDUM OF AGREEMENT made the...................................day of.....................................

BETWEEN:

....

(hereinafter called 'the Client') of the one part

(of) (whose registered office is at) ....

....

and

....

(hereinafter called 'the Project Manager') of the other part

(of) (whose registered office is at) ....

....

WHEREAS

*A The Client intends to proceed with..

....

....

(referred to in this Agreement as 'the Project') and has requested the Project Manager to provide professional services as referred to in the Conditions of Engagement and Appendices attached hereto (referred to in this Agreement as 'the Services').

B   The Client intends to appoint other consultants to provide other services in connection with the project.

NOW IT IS HEREBY AGREED as follows:

1   The client agrees to engage the project manager subject to and in accordance with the *Conditions of Engagement* attached hereto and the project manager agrees to provide the services set out in *Appendix A* subject to and in accordance with the said *Conditions of Engagement*.

2   The project manager shall act as the agent of the client, and be responsible for the administration, management and communication co-ordination of the project, but nevertheless shall not without the express prior written consent of the project manager also be appointed or designated as 'agent' for the purpose of performing the duties imposed on the client by The Construction (Design and Management) Regulations 1994.

Be sure to complete every clause which has an asterisk

3 The project manager shall:
   (a) communicate to the consultants the requirements of the client's brief;
   (b) monitor the progress of design work and the achievement of function by reference to the client's brief;
   (c) monitor and regulate programme and progress;
   (d) monitor and use his reasonable endeavours to co-ordinate the efforts of all consultants, advisers, contractors and suppliers directly connected with the project;
   (e) monitor the cost and financial rewards of the project by reference to the client's brief;
   (f) advise the client with regard to the general application of the Construction (Design and Management) Regulations and comply with Regulation 13 (1);
   (g) advise client with regard to the obligations under Housing Grants, Construction and Regeneration Act 1996, regarding payment and rights to an arbitrator.

4 Project manager's authority to instruct

4.1 The project manager shall not without the prior written consent of the client give to the main or any other contractor or any supplier or any other person any instruction the necessary effect of which would be materially either to vary the project or to increase the cost of or the time taken to complete the project.

4.2 The project manager shall promptly inform the client in writing of anything the likely effect of which the project manager believes would be materially either:
   (a) to vary the project; or
   (b) to increase the cost of the project or change its financial viability, quality or function; or
   (c) to increase the time taken to complete the project.

5 The project manager shall not be responsible for:
   (a) any forecasts of financial viability unless prepared by him or her;
   (b) the consultant's designs and technical co-ordination thereof;
   (c) the advice or recommendations that may be provided by any consultant or adviser appointed by the client.

6 Project manager's liability

6.1 The project manager shall perform the services with reasonable skill care and diligence, but the liability of the project manager for the project manager's own acts and omissions whether in contract or in tort or otherwise for any loss, injury or damage sustained shall be limited in each of the following respects:
   (a) the project manager shall not in any event be liable for more than the project manager's just and equitable proportionate share of the loss, injury or damage assuming that all others responsible were equally obliged to exercise reasonable skill, care and diligence and have paid their just and equitable proportionate shares.
   *(b) The project manager shall not in any event be liable for more than an aggregate sum of £................... including any contractual or statutory interest.
   *(c) The project manager shall not in any event be liable unless proceedings by way of court action or for arbitration or for alternative dispute resolution have been commenced within .... years from completion of the project manager's services as defined in clause 10c or any revised date for completion of the project manager's services as may be agreed and confirmed in writing between the client and the project manager.
   *(d) Professional indemnity insurance referred to in clause 15 of the *Conditions of Engagement* shall be effected for a sum of not less than £...................

6.2 No liability shall attach to the project manager either in contract or in tort or otherwise for loss, injury or damage sustained as a result of any defect in any material or the act, omission or insolvency of any person other than the project manager and the project manager shall not be liable to indemnify the client in respect of any claim made against the client for any such loss, injury or damage.

6.3 None of clauses 6.1(a) to (c) or 6.2 above shall be valid insofar as prohibited by statute.

7   The *Memorandum of Agreement* and the said *Conditions of Engagement* shall together constitute the agreement between the client and the project manager. Any variation thereof after the date of this agreement shall only be by written consent of the parties.

*8   The date of commencement of this agreement shall be ....

*9   The period of delay referred to in clause 5.6 of the *Conditions of Engagement* shall be

     ....

*10   (a)   The client shall pay to the project manager the fee of .... for the services listed in *Appendix A* of the *Conditions of Engagement*.
           (b)   Payment of the fee shall be made in accordance with Appendix C of the *Conditions of*
*   *Engagement*.
           (c)   The date for completion of the services, beyond which the fee is to be adjusted as
*   provided in clause 7.9 of the *Conditions of Engagement* is ....
           (d)   The rate of interest referred to in clause 7.6 of the *Conditions of Engagement* is .... per cent.

*11   The project manager will appoint .... as the principal person employed by the project manager who will undertake the direction and control of the project manager's duties and obligations under this agreement (subject to the provisions of clause 3.3 of the *Conditions of Engagement*).

*12   Any collateral warranty entered into pursuant to clause 4 of the *Conditions of Engagement*:
- shall be in the form published by the British Property Federation;
- may not be assigned more than ....times;
- shall specify as the sum for which professional indemnity insurance is required the sum of £..............
- shall specify as the period for which insurance shall be maintained, and as a limitation period within which proceeding by way of court action or for arbitration or for alternative dispute resolution must have been commenced a period of .... years.

13   For the avoidance of doubt the obligations, liabilities and responsibilities of the project manager are as expressly stated herein. No additional obligations, liabilities or responsibilities whatsoever shall be implied.

14   No indulgence shown by either the client or the project manager shall prevent the other subsequently insisting upon their rights and remedies under the agreement.

*15   The provision for the exercise of the right to refer a dispute to adjudication set out in The Scheme for Construction Contracts (England and Wales) Regulations 1998, Part 1, shall apply, for which purpose the adjudicator shall be

     (name).. of

     (contact address)..

     or if unwilling or unable to act, or nobody is named, an individual nominated for the purpose by a Vice-President for the time being of The Royal Institution of Chartered Surveyors.

AS WITNESS the hands of the parties the date first written above.

Duly authorised representative of the Client: ....

Witness: ....

Address: ....

Duly authorised representative of the Project Manager:...

Witness: ....

Address: ....

OR if as a DEED:

Executed and delivered as a DEED by .... Limited/plc in the presence of:

Director:...

Secretary: ....

Executed and delivered as a DEED by .... Limited/plc in the presence of:

Director:...

Secretary: ....

SIGNED AND DELIVERED AS A DEED BY THE SAID .... (Signature)

[insert full names here]

....

In the presence of: (Full Name)

Witness's Signature

Witness's Full Name

Address: ....

....

....

Occupation:...

SIGNED AND DELIVERED AS A DEED BY THE SAID .... (Signature)

[insert full names here]

....

In the presence of: (Full Name)

Witness's Signature

Witness's Full Name

Address: ....

....

....

Occupation:...

Conditions of Engagement for a Professional Project Manager

• GENERAL CONDITIONS

1 Definitions

In this agreement the following terms shall have the meaning hereby assigned:

- 'The Client' - the person or company named in the *Memorandum of Agreement*;
- 'The Project Manager' - the person or company named in the *Memorandum of Agreement*;
- 'The Consultant' - any or all of the consultants appointed by the client to undertake specialist design and other functions in connection with the project;
- 'The Project' - the project with which the client is proceeding and for which the services of the project manager have been engaged;
- 'The Brief' - the written brief provided by the client to the project manager prior to the date of this agreement to describe the objectives of time cost quality and function of the project;
- 'The Services' - the services to be provided by the project manager and identified in this agreement.

2 Schedule of services

2.1 The services to be provided by the project manager have been listed in *Appendix A*.

2.2 Additional services may from time to time be agreed between the parties. Any adjustment of payment to the project manager under clause 7.1 shall be agreed at the time.

3 Project manager's staff

3.1 The person named in clause 11 of the *Memorandum of Agreement* shall have full authority on behalf of the project manager.

3.2 The person named in clause 11 of the *Memorandum of Agreement* shall not be changed without the written consent of the client. The replacement shall be approved by the client in writing. Consent for the change, and approval of the replacement shall not be unreasonably withheld.

3.3 The client may request the replacement of the person named in clause 11. The replacement shall be a member of the organisation named as project manager. The client shall approve the replacement in writing, and approval shall not be unreasonably withheld.

4 Collateral warranty

4.1 Upon the written request of the client, the project manager shall for a consideration or by deed execute a collateral warranty in the form stated in Clause 12 of the *Memorandum of Agreement* in favour of each and any third party who takes an estate interest in the project.

4.2 Such written request by the client may be served at any time but no later than the end of the period of two years from the date when the project manager last performed any of the services.

4.3 Nothing in clause 4.1 above shall give to such third party any right to direct or control the project manager in the performance of the services.

5 Duration of engagement

5.1 The appointment shall commence from the date stated in clause 8 of the *Memorandum of Agreement*.

5.2 The benefits and obligations of this agreement may be assigned by either party but only with the prior written consent of the other.

5.3 The client may terminate this appointment at any time by notice in writing. Upon termination the client shall make a payment in accordance with clause 11.1.

5.4 The client may postpone the project and shall confirm such instruction in writing. Upon postponement the client shall make a payment in accordance with clause 11.1.

5.5 If, following postponement, there is no resumption within six months, this appointment shall be automatically terminated.

5.6 The project manager may terminate this agreement if the project is delayed and he or she is prevented from carrying out his or her services for a period of more than that stated in clause 9 of the *Memorandum of Agreement*.

5.7 Either party shall be entitled forthwith to terminate this agreement by written notice to the other if:

5.7.1 that other party commits any breach of any of the provisions of this agreement and, in the case of a breach capable of remedy, fails to remedy the same within 30 days after receipt of a written notice giving full particulars of the breach and requiring it to be remedied;

5.7.2 that other party makes any voluntary arrangement with its creditors or becomes subject to an administration order;

5.7.3 that other party goes into liquidation unless it did so for the purpose of amalgamation or reconstruction and the amalgamated or reconstructed company has assumed this agreement;

5.7.4 anything analogous to any of the foregoing under the law of any jurisdiction occurs in relation to that other party;

5.7.5 that other party ceases or threatens to cease to carry on business.

5.8 For the purposes of clause 5.7.1 a breach shall be considered capable of remedy if the party in breach can comply with the provision in question in all respects other than as to the time of performance (provided that time of performance is not of the essence),

5.9 Any waiver by either party of a breach of any provision of this agreement shall not be considered as a waiver of any subsequent breach of the same or any other provision thereof.

5.10 The rights to terminate this agreement given by clause 5.7 shall be without prejudice to any other right or remedy of either party in respect of the breach concerned (if any) or any other breach. Upon termination the client shall make payment in accordance with clause 12.

6 The obligations of the client

6.1 The client shall provide the project manager with a written brief.

6.2 The client shall ensure that all information reasonably required by the project manager from the client or obtainable by the client is provided to the project manager when required without charge. The client shall give written consent to those matters listed in *Appendix B* when required, to enable the project manager to discharge his or her duties. The client shall provide everything reasonably necessary to enable the project manager to discharge their duties.

6.3 The client shall procure the services of, and directly appoint, other consultants to the project. The project manager shall be responsible for the management of the consultants as identified by this agreement, but no direct contract will exist between the project manager and the other consultants. The *Conditions of Engagement* for such consultants shall include provision that information required by the project manager in the performance of his or her duties is provided when reasonably required without charge to the project manager.

6.4 The client shall formally notify the consultants of the authority given to the project manager to act on behalf of the client in the performance of the project manager's duties under this agreement, subject to the requirement to obtain written consent to the items listed in *Appendix B*.

6.5 The client shall nominate to the project manager the person within the client's organization to whom the project manager is to report.

6.6 The client shall advise the project manager of the client's corporate or other arrangements for providing the authorities set out in *Appendix B*.

7 Payment

7.1 The project manager's fee for the services provided under this agreement is stated in the *Memorandum of Agreement*.

7.2 The client shall pay the project manager for the performance of the services the fees and charges in accordance with the schedule of payments set out in *Appendix C*. The 'due date for payment' shall be 7 (seven) days (see clause 16 below) after the date of the submission of the invoice. The project manager when submitting their invoice shall on each invoice state the basis on which the stated amount is calculated.

7.3 The 'final date for payment' shall be 21 (twenty-one) days after the due date for payment. Payment shall be made not later than the final date for payment.

7.4 The client may, not later than 5 (five) days after the due date for payment, give to the project manager written notice stating the amount which the client proposes to pay and the basis on which that amount is calculated. Where no such notice is given the amount to be paid is that stated in the invoice.

7.5 Where the client intends to withhold payment of any amount stated in the project manager's invoice or in a written notice given by the client under clause 7.4 above, the client must give written notice to the project manager not later than 5 (five) days before the final date for payment, stating the amount to be withheld and the grounds for withholding payment.

7.6 Any amounts due to the project manager under this agreement which remain unpaid by the client after the final date for payment shall bear interest at the rate stated in the *Memorandum of Agreement*.

7.7 In the event that the client is in default over payment of amounts at the final date for payment and no notice of intention to withhold payment from such amount has been given under clause 7.5 above, the project manager may suspend performance of any or all the services. This right is subject to the project manager first giving the client not less than 7 (seven) days' written notice of such intention and stating the grounds for suspension. The right to suspend performance shall cease when the client makes payment of the amount due. Any such period of suspension shall be disregarded for the purposes of contractual time limits previously agreed for the completion of the services. Such suspension shall not be treated as a suspension under clause 5.4. This provision shall not prejudice the right of the project manager to terminate their appointment under clause 5.7. Any disputed amounts shall not entitle the client to withhold payment of undisputed amounts.

7.8 The project manager shall notify the client in writing as soon as it becomes reasonably apparent that any work additional to the subject of this agreement will be required.

7.9 The fee is calculated assuming completion of the project by the date stated in clause 10 (c) of the *Memorandum of Agreement.* If the project is extended by agreement between the parties beyond this date, the fee shall be adjusted in accordance with the provisions included in *Appendix D* (lump sum fee).

7.10 All fees in this agreement exclude VAT. All VAT properly due shall be paid by the client to the project manager. On written demand by the client the project manager shall provide VAT invoices in proper form.

8 Payment for additional services

If an additional service is required, the project manager shall notify the client in writing of the fact. If required he or she shall furnish written quotations. The fee for any such additional services if agreed shall be treated as a variation and added to the total fee payable and the provisions of clause 7 shall apply thereto.

9 Goods, equipment and services

The client shall be responsible for the cost of provision and maintenance of all goods, material, equipment and services as listed in *Appendix E.*

10 Expenses

The fee stated in clause 10(a) of the *Memorandum of Agreement* shall be inclusive of all disbursements and expenses save those listed in *Appendix F.*

11 Payment following termination or suspension by the client

11.1 Following termination by the client under clause 5.3 or postponement under clause 5.4, the client shall pay to the project manager:

a) a fair proportion of the fee payable at the date of termination for services provided, payable under this agreement such proportion to be calculated by reference to *Appendix C.*
b) the reasonably and properly incurred costs of the project manager resulting from this termination or postponement.

11.2 The client may issue a written order to resume within six months of termination or postponement. The fee shall be that due under this agreement plus costs under clause 11.1(b) plus an agreed fee for any additional costs and services in connection with the resumption.

11.3 If the duties of the project manager cannot be discharged for reasons outside the control of the client or the project manager, the appointment shall be treated as terminated. The project manager shall be entitled to appropriate payment under clauses 11.1(a) and 11.1(b).

12 Payment following termination by the project manager

Upon termination of an appointment under clause 5.6 or 5.7 the project manager shall be entitled to payment under clauses 11.1(a) and 11.1(b). Payment is without prejudice to any other rights and remedies of either party.

13 Complaints

In the event that the client has a complaint in respect of the performance of the project manager's services under this agreement, without prejudice to any other remedy available under this agreement, they shall be entitled to have access to the complaints handling procedure maintained by the project manager, written copies of which should be available on request from the project manager.

14 Settlement of disputes

If a dispute arises out of this agreement, the client and the project manager shall attempt to agree a settlement in good faith.

14.1 If the dispute is not thus resolved either the client or the project manager may at any time give notice to the other in writing that they wish to refer the dispute to an adjudicator. The person who is to act as the adjudicator shall be agreed between the client and project manager within 2 (two) days of such notice having been given or failing agreement be a person appointed by the President or Vice-President of the Chartered Institute of Arbitrators within 5 (five) days of such notice having been given. The referring party shall refer the dispute in writing to the adjudicator within 7 (seven) days of such notice having been given.

14.2 The adjudication shall be conducted in accordance with the Construction Industry Council Model Adjudication Procedures current at the time notice of the dispute is given. Clause 30 of the Construction Industry Council Model Adjudication Procedures shall be amended to add the following sentence:

14.3 'No party shall be entitled to raise any right of set off, counterclaim and abatement/or connection with any enforcement proceedings.'

14.4 The adjudicator shall act impartially and may take the initiative in ascertaining the facts and the law.
The adjudicator shall reach a decision:
a) within 28 (twenty-eight) days of the referral of the dispute to the adjudicator, or
b) within 42 (forty-two) days of the referral of the dispute to the adjudicator if the referring party so consents, or
c) in a period exceeding 28 (twenty-eight) days from referral of the dispute to the adjudicator as the client and the project manager may agree after such referral.

14.5 The adjudicator is not liable for anything they do or omit to do in the discharge or purported discharge of their function as adjudicator unless the act or omission is in bad faith. Any employee or agent of the adjudicator shall be similarly protected from liability.

14.6 The decision of the adjudicator shall, subject to the provisions of clauses 14.8, 14.9. and 14.10, be binding until the dispute is finally determined by arbitration.

14.7 The client and the project manager may agree to accept the decision of the adjudicator as finally determining the dispute.

14.8 If the client or the project manager is dissatisfied with the decision of the adjudicator then:

14.9 The dispute may be determined by agreement between the parties, or

14.10 The dispute may be referred at the instance of either party to be determined by an arbitrator in accordance with Clause 15 below.

15 Arbitration

The person who is to act as an arbitrator shall be agreed between the parties within 28 (twenty-eight) days of the one giving the other written notice of their wish to refer the decision to an arbitrator, or failing agreement at the end of that period shall be a person appointed by the President or Vice-President of The Chartered Institute of Arbitrators at the instance of either party.

16 Notices

All notices and other communications shall be in writing and shall be deemed to have been duly given: when delivered if delivered by messenger during normal business hours of recipient; when sent if transmitted by telex or facsimile transmission (receipt confirmed) during normal business hours of the recipient or on the third business day following mailing if mailed by certified or registered mail postage pre-paid in each case addressed to each party's registered office or any other address notified to each other in writing as an address to which notices, invoices and other documents should be sent.

Where under this agreement an act is required to be done within a specified period of days after or from a specified date, the period shall begin immediately after that date. Where the period would include a day which is Christmas Day, Good Friday or a day which under Banking and Financial Dealings Act 1971 is a Bank Holiday, that day shall be excluded.

17 Professional indemnity insurance

The project manager shall effect a professional indemnity insurance for the figure stated in clause 6.1(d) of the *Memorandum of Agreement* for each and every claim and if necessary provide evidence of such insurance having been effected, and further shall maintain professional indemnity insurance so long as it remains available at reasonable rates in the market.

18 Copyright

The copyright in all reports, models, specifications, bills of quantities, calculations and other documents and information prepared by or on behalf of the project manager in connection with the project (together referred to in this clause 16 as the 'documents') shall remain vested in the project manager, but subject of the project manager having received payment of any fees agreed as properly due under the agreement, the client shall have a licence to copy and use the documents and to reproduce the content of them for any purpose relating to the project including but without limitation, the construction, completion, maintenance, letting, promotion, advertisement, reinstatement, refurbishment and repair of the project. The project manager shall not be liable for the use by the client of any of the documents for any purpose other than that for which the same were prepared by or on behalf of the project manager.

19 Law

English Law shall apply to this agreement.

APPENDIX A

Schedule of Services

APPENDIX B

The Schedule of Matters in Connection with the Project Requiring the Written Consent of the Client before Proceeding under Clause 6.2

APPENDIX C

The Schedule of Payments

APPENDIX D

Provision for Adjustment of Fee in Accordance with Clause 7.9

APPENDIX E

The Schedule of Site Office Accommodation, Furniture, Telephones, Other
Equipment and Services in Accordance with Clause 9

APPENDIX F

The Schedule of Disbursements and Expenses Referred to in Clause 10